JAMES PATTERSON

WITCH & WIZARD

BATTLE FOR SHADOWLAND

JAMES PATTERSON
WITCH & WIZARD
BATTLE FOR SHADOWLAND

Special thanks to Leopoldo Gout, Steve Bowen, Gabrielle Charbonnet, and James Patterson.

www.**IDWPUBLISHING**.com

ISBN: 978-1-60010-930-0   13 12 11 10   1 2 3 4

™ IDW Publishing is: Operations: Ted Adams, CEO & Publisher • Greg Goldstein, Chief Operating Officer • Matthew Ruzicka, CPA, Chief Financial Officer • Alan Payne, VP of Sales • Lorelei Bunjes, Director of Digital Services • Jeff Webber, Director of ePublishing • AnnaMaria White, Dir, Marketing and Public Relations • Dirk Wood, Dir, Retail Marketing • Marci Hubbard, Executive Assistant • Alonzo Simon, Shipping Manager • Angela Loggins, Staff Accountant • Cherrie Go, Assistant Web Designer • Editorial: Chris Ryall, Chief Creative Officer, Editor-In-Chief • Scott Dunbier, Senior Editor, Special Projects • Andy Schmidt, Senior Editor • Bob Schreck, Senior Editor • Justin Eisinger, Senior Editor, Books • Kris Oprisko, Editor/Foreign Lic. • Denton J. Tipton, Editor • Tom Waltz, Editor • Mariah Huehner, Editor • Carlos Guzman, Assistant Editor • Bobby Curnow, Assistant Editor • Design: Robbie Robbins, EVP/Sr. Graphic Artist • Neil Uyetake, Senior Art Director • Chris Mowry, Senior Graphic Artist • Amauri Osorio, Graphic Artist • Gilberto Lazcano, Production Assistant • Shawn Lee, Graphic Artist

WRITERS
JAMES PATTERSON
AND DARA NARAGHI

ARTIST
VICTOR SANTOS

COLORIST
JAMIE GRANT

LETTERERS
CHRIS MOWRY & NEIL UYETAKE

SERIES EDITOR
BOB SCHRECK

COLLECTION EDITOR
JUSTIN EISINGER

COLLECTION DESIGNER
NEIL UYETAKE

WITCH & WIZARD CREATED BY JAMES PATTERSON

Excerpts from "The Supreme Ascendancy of the New Order: A Brief History", pp. 58-72, by The One Who Records History, © 0001 A.O., New Order Press.

For the exclusive use of New Order Reformatory guests.

[handwritten: i.e. prisoners!]

In retrospect, it is a simple task to identify the driving force behind the rise in popularity of the New Order political party. The people of this failed country, disillusioned by their so-called democracy and freedoms, embraced the values and principles of the New Order. This was a populist movement, a higher discipline led by smart, visionary leaders with a plan for a bright new future for every man, woman, and child.

[handwritten: What a joke! It was a total con job by a power-hungry evil sociopath]

And so it was that on the first day of the first year of the New Order's Supreme Ascendancy, The Council Of Ones was established. Led by The One Who Is The One – our benevolent and capable leader – The Council took the necessary steps to elevate this nation to its rightful moral, cultural, and technological supremacy. This was achieved through a series of decrees designed to eliminate the corrupting influences of the old world. Superfluous and undesirable distractions such as art, music, and books were outlawed for the greater good of society.* Above all, the practice of the Foul Arts was strictly forbidden to all.

[handwritten: The aforementioned power-hungry evil sociopath]

[handwritten: Yeah, as long as you obey their orders like a good little robot]

[handwritten: i.e. totalitarian state!]

[handwritten: i.e. everything worth living for, including freedom.]

While these laws are supported unanimously by the citizenry, they are occasionally violated by deviants and criminals. Such offenders are treated sternly, yet with compassion, and are cured of their antisocial behaviors, returning to the populace as a capable and contributing member of society.

[handwritten: We're just kids!]

[handwritten: Meaning Magic, although it's funny how The One uses Magic himself]

*See also: The One Who Writes New Laws, The One Who Judges, The One Who Imprisons, et al.

[handwritten: There's no "returning" from an execution]

Suggested further reading: "Benjamin, Eliza, Whitford, and Wisteria: The Allgood Family of Deviants", by The One Who Hunts Fugitives.

[handwritten: i.e. kangaroo court, show trial, etc.]

[handwritten: Stay strong, mom and dad! We love you]

WE'VE TAKEN REFUGE IN *FREELAND*. ESSENTIALLY ONE OF THE MANY OLD CITIES RAZED BY THE N.O. AND NOT YET REBUILT IN THEIR *IDEAL* IMAGE.

THE KIDS IN THE RESISTANCE HAVE TURNED AN OLD DEPARTMENT STORE INTO THEIR MAKESHIFT HEADQUARTERS.

GARFUNKLE'S

GARFUNKLE'S

WHICH IS WHERE THIS WHOLE MESS WAS SET IN MOTION, WITH THAT FATEFUL MESSAGE ON THE *PROPHECY WALL*.

YEAH, IT'S PRETTY MUCH WHAT IT SOUNDS LIKE: A MYSTICAL *INSTANT* MESSAGE OF PREDICTIONS AND DIRECTIONS. ON A WALL.

DATA CENTER @ COLUMBUS AND 4TH ST.
RETRIEVE-DISK-ARRAY R614

HUH, THAT'S A NEW ONE.

THAT'S JAMILLA, OUR *"THIS WEEK'S LEADER."*

SEE, UNLIKE THE ADULTS WHO HAVE RUN THE WORLD INTO THE GROUND, THESE KIDS ARE *SMART*. THEY KNOW THAT *POWER CORRUPTS...*

MANAGER

...SO THEY'VE DECIDED TO **ROTATE** THE LEADERSHIP POSITION EVERY WEEK, TO MAKE SURE NOBODY GETS TOO COMFORTABLE IN THEIR POSITION OF AUTHORITY.

THE BUILDING IS A DATA CENTER, WHERE THE N.O. KEEPS BACKUPS OF ALL THEIR FILES. WHATEVER'S ON THAT DRIVE MUST BE IMPORTANT, SO I WANT YOU TO BREAK IN AND STEAL IT.

YEAH, I KNOW THAT PLACE. WE GOT A TOUR OF IT WHEN I WAS GOING THROUGH **JUNIOR INFORMANT** TRAINING.

THAT'S ALL THE MORE REASON **NOT** TO TAKE MR. WEASEL MCSPY WITH US.

BYRON SWAIN WAS THE SNITCH CLASSMATE WHO TURNED US IN TO THE N.O.

LOOK, I KNOW WHAT I DID TO YOU GUYS WAS INEXCUSABLE, BUT I'M ON YOUR SIDE NOW. I'M TRYING TO HELP.

YEAH, WHATEVER. HELP YOUR **BALD BOSS** CATCH US, MORE LIKE IT.

THAT'S NOT FAIR. I—

BUT HE CLAIMS TO HAVE REFORMED, AND US ALLGOODS ARE SUCKERS FOR **SECOND CHANCES.** STILL, MY SISTER CAN HOLD A GRUDGE WITH THE BEST OF THEM.

ENOUGH. YOU'LL NEED ALL THE INSIDE INFO YOU CAN USE ON THIS MISSION, SO BYRON GOES WITH YOU.

WE RAIDED THE AUTOMOTIVE DEPARTMENT AND MANAGED TO REPAIR THE VAN YOU GUYS **"LIBERATED"** FROM THE N.O., SO YOU'LL HAVE TRANSPORTATION.

I'LL HAVE ONE OF THE **CURVES** FIND A **PORTAL** THAT PUTS YOU CLOSE TO THE TARGET.

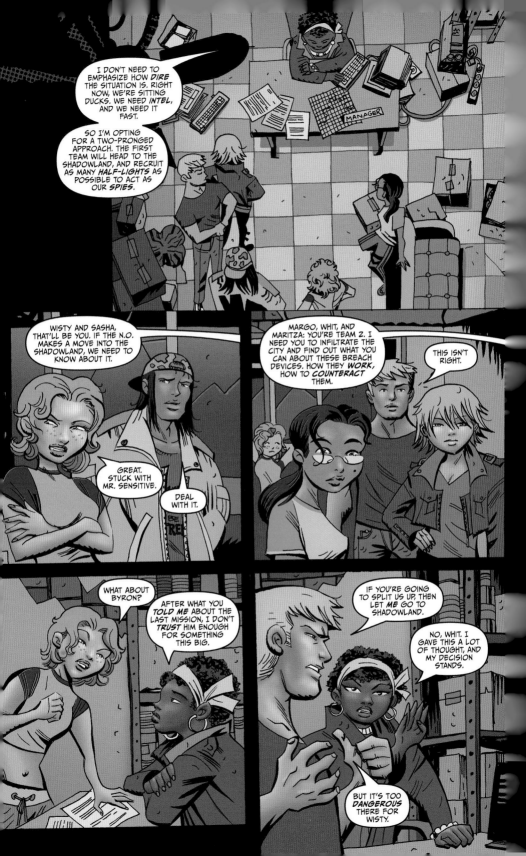

WISTY'S TEAM HAD TO WALK 2 MILES TO FIND A PORTAL TO SHADOWLAND.

WE LUCKED OUT AND FOUND A NEW ONE TO THE CITY OF PROGRESS FORMING JUST A BLOCK DOWN FROM GARFUNKLE'S.

AS ALWAYS, MARGO TOOK THE LEAD. 'FIRST IN, LAST OUT' HAS ALWAYS BEEN HER MANTRA.

TO FIT IN, THE GIRLS JUST HAD TO CLEAN UP AND CHANGE CLOTHES. I, ON THE OTHER HAND, AM A RECOGNIZABLE FUGITIVE, SO I HAD TO ALTER MY LOOKS WITH A BIT OF MAGIC.

REMEMBER, THE GOAL IS TO *BLEND IN* WITH THE OTHER STRAIGHT-AND-NARROWS. KEEP YOUR COOL, AND FOLLOW THE PLAN.

THE CITY OF PROGRESS. THE NEW ORDER'S STRONGHOLD. ALL OTHER CITIES WILL BE REBUILT IN ITS IMAGE.

THIS PLACE GIVES ME THE *CREEPS*, WHIT.

CHAPTER TWO

SHADOWLAND.

THE CITY OF PROGRESS.

MISTY

THE **SECOND** SCARIEST THING ABOUT SHADOWLAND IS HOW EASILY YOU COULD GET **LOST** OUT HERE. THERE ARE NO LANDMARKS, NO GEOGRAPHICAL FEATURES.

I ASKED FOR YOUR ID, **CITIZEN.**

WHIT

OH NO! **FIGURES** WE'D RUN INTO A **CITIZEN PATROL.** NOTHING BUT A BUNCH OF **STATE-SANCTIONED THUGS.**

WE NEED A **COVER STORY.** THINK, WHIT, THINK.

THE **SCARIEST** THING, HOWEVER, IS RUNNING INTO THOSE POOR HUMANS WHO **DID** GET LOST. AFTER A WHILE, ALL THAT'S LEFT OF THEM IS **CROOKED** AND **BENT** HUSKS KNOWN AS THE **LOST ONES.**

WELL, SIR... YOU SEE—

AND THEY WANT NOTHING MORE THAN TO **FEAST** ON THE **FLESH** OF THOSE OF US STILL AMONGST THE **LIVING.**

THE CITY OF PROGRESS.

I ONCE USED MY MAGIC TO *STOP* A JUDGE'S GAVEL IN *MID-AIR*, AFTER HE THREW IT AT MY HEAD.

SO IT SHOULDN'T BE TOO HARD *LIFTING* A COUPLE OF BADGES *DISCREETLY*.

HEY, WHAT THE—?

OOPS, SO MUCH FOR SUBTLETY.

TIME FOR *PLAN B*.

SORRY ABOUT THE HEADACHE, GUYS.

THERE! NOW WE CAN WALK RIGHT THROUGH THE *FRONT ENTRANCE*.

GREAT, EXCEPT THERE'S *THREE* OF US AND ONLY *TWO* BADGES!

YEAH, SO WHAT *NOW*, THE ONE WHO CAN'T COUNT?

UH...

SHADOWLAND.

TRUE TO HIS WORD, MORRIS ROUNDED UP A BUNCH OF HIS HALF-LIGHT FRIENDS TO HELP WITH OUR CAUSE. IT WAS DEFINITELY AN *IMPRESSIVE* START FOR OUR LITTLE SPY NETWORK.

YOU KNOW, ONCE YOU GOT *PAST* THE FACT THAT THESE WERE ALL KIDS *MURDERED* BY THE NEW ORDER.

TO MAKE MATTERS WORSE, I COULDN'T HELP BUT NOTICE *CELIA* WAS NOWHERE TO BE FOUND.

I *DREAD* GIVING WHIT THE NEWS.

GREAT, AND HERE COMES 'MR. ANYTHING FOR THE CAUSE' TO *TAKE CHARGE* AGAIN.

HEY, WISTY... I THINK WE'RE ALL SET. READY TO HEAD BACK TO *GARFUNKLE'S?*

QUICK, MORRIS NEEDS YOU GUYS! THERE'S SOMETHING *STRANGE* HAPPENING!

MORRIS, WHAT IS IT?

CHAPTER THREE

SHADOWLAND.

WISTY

THEY JUST *KILLED* SASHA!

I'M ON MY OWN.

LUCKILY FOR ME, I HAVE TWO THINGS GOING FOR ME. *ONE;* I KNOW THEY HAVE ORDERS *NOT* TO KILL ME. FOR WHATEVER REASON, *THE ONE* WANTS ME ALIVE.

OK, GIRL. PUT THESE ON, NICE AND EASY.

AND *TWO;* MARGO TAUGHT ME A THING OR TWO ABOUT *FIGHTING DIRTY.*

YOU WISH.

UNF.

OH, RIGHT. FORGOT THERE'S ALSO A *THREE;* GOOD OL' FEFFER.

THE BUILDING OF SCIENCE.

WHIT

WE'VE JUST BEEN *CAPTURED* BY THE ONE WHO IS THE ONE.

YOU AND YOUR SISTER HAVE BEEN *ANNOYING* THORNS IN MY SIDE, WHIT. IT'LL BE A PLEASURE TO FINALLY *PLUCK* YOU OUT.

HE STANDS THERE, GLOATING. COCKY.

BIG MISTAKE.

HE JUST BOUGHT ME THE FEW SECONDS I NEEDED TO *CATCH MY BREATH.*

DRIVEN BY RAGE, I *SUMMON* EVERY BIT OF MAGIC THAT I CAN.

YOU'RE GOING DOWN!

FREELAND.

AT THE MISSION *DEBRIEF*, JAMILLA DID HER BEST TO REMAIN *STOIC* WHEN FACED WITH THE NEWS OF MARITZA'S MURDER.

IN FACT, SHE WAS ALL BUSINESS.

WE NEED TO CONVENE A *WAR COUNCIL* AND PLAN OUR NEXT MOVE, AS SOON AS MARGO'S RESTED AND SASHA'S BACK.

THAT'S WEIRD, HE SHOULD BE HERE *BY NOW*.

SPEAKING OF WHICH, I *STILL* CAN'T FIGURE OUT HOW YOU WERE IN THE CITY AT THE *SAME TIME* AS US, WISTY.

IT'S A LITTLE HARD TO EXPLAIN...

...SASHA AND I WERE IN SHADOWLAND FOR A *LONG TIME*. AFTER I SENT ALL THE N.O. TROOPS... UM, *AWAY*, I PASSED OUT.

NEAR AS I CAN FIGURE, FEFFER DRAGGED ME INTO A PORTAL AND OUT OF THERE. GUESS IT PAYS TO HAVE A *CURVE DOG*, HUH?

BUT WHEN I *CAME TO*, I FOUND MYSELF IN THE CITY OF PROGRESS. OUT OF THE FIRE AND INTO THE FRYING PAN, RIGHT?

NO

ANYWAY, THE FIRST THING I DID WAS *DISGUISE* MY LOOKS, WHAT WITH ME BEING A KNOWN *FUGITIVE* AND ALL.

THEN I SET OUT TO FIND A PORTAL BACK TO FREELAND, BUT IMAGINE MY *SURPRISE*...

CHAPTER FOUR

NEEDLESS TO SAY, THE BATTLE PREPARATIONS HAD PUT MOST OF THE KIDS IN A PANIC.

BUT JAMILLA HANDLED IT ALL SO WELL. SHE ORGANIZED A SMALL *MEMORIAL* TO HONOR MARITZA, WHICH ALSO SERVED TO KEEP THE KIDS CALM AND *FOCUSED*.

MARITZA GUTIERREZ WAS MORE THAN JUST A VALUABLE MEMBER OF OUR RESISTANCE, SHE WAS OUR *FRIEND*. HER SHARP INTELLECT WAS ONLY SURPASSED BY HER *KIND HEART*.

A HEART THAT STOPPED BEATING AT THE HANDS OF THE ONE WHO IS THE ONE. A HEART THAT WAS *ROBBED* OF LIFE, LOVE, JOY, AND ENDLESS POTENTIAL.

BUT A HEART THAT WILL LIVE ON FOREVER, IN *OUR* HEARTS.

MANAGER

WE'LL MISS YOU, MARITZA. WHICH IS WHY WE'LL *NEVER* STOP FIGHTING THE NEW ORDER UNTIL THERE'S *JUSTICE* FOR YOU, AND *ALL* OUR LOST FRIENDS.

GONE BUT NEVER FORGOTTEN

I LOVE YOU BROTHER

WE MISS YOU RAUL

NOW, I NEED EVERYONE WITH *MAGICAL ABILITIES* TO MEET UP ON THE ROOF TO HELP WHIT AND WISTY WITH A CRUCIAL SPELL.

THE REST OF YOU, FIND ANYTHING THAT CAN BE USED AS A *WEAPON* AND ASSEMBLE BY THE LOADING DOCKS.

WELL, HERE WE GO. I SURE HOPE IT WORKS.

ME TOO.

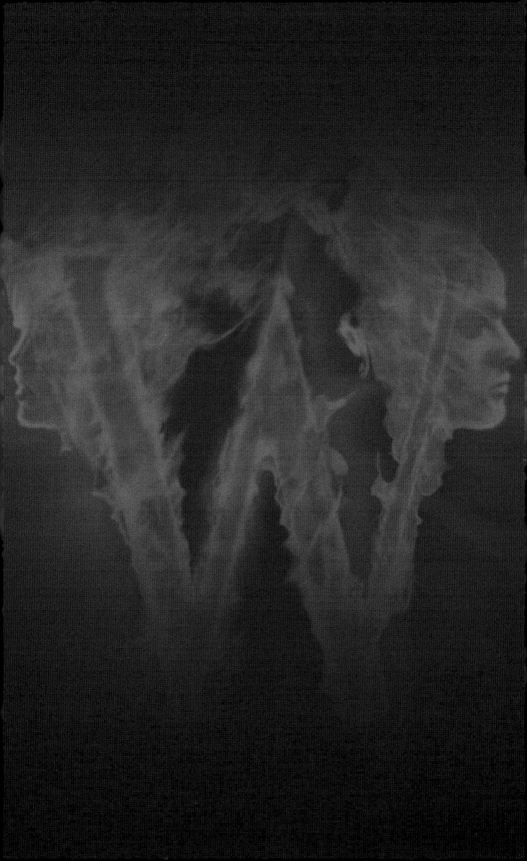

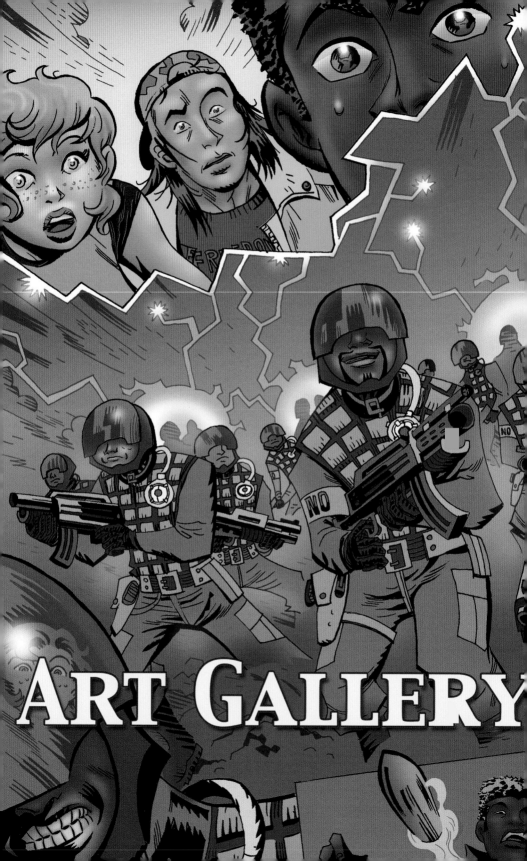

ART BY J.K. WOODWARD

ART BY FABIO MOON

ART BY Fabio Moon

ART BY FABIO MOON

CHARACTER SKETCHES
BY VICTOR SANTOS

MORRIS

MARITZA

OTHER GLASSES

BENJAMIN & ELIZA ALLGOOD

CELIA

"WISTY" ALLGOOD

VICTOR SANTOS

or

MORE SPORTY

"WHIT" ALLGOOD

VICTOR SANTOS

SOME KIND
OF YOUNG
JENSEN ACKELS
(SUPERNATURAL)

WITCH
&
WIZARD
DESIGNS
14/1/10

CALCETIN
BLANCO

GRIS

JAMILLA

BYRON SWAIN

NEW ORDER
COMMANDOS

CITIZEN PATROL

FEFFER
(GERMAN SHEPHERD)

N.O.

N.O.

FREEDO SHOULD BE FREE

SASHA
VICTOR SANTOS

MARGO
VICTOR SANTOS
THE TOUGH GIRL

TOO MUCH FOR A TEEN BOOK?

THE ONE WHO IS THE ONE
VICTOR SANTOS

THE ONE WHO CREATES NEW WEAPONS
VICTOR SANTOS